THE TOP TEN CONTEMPORARY CLASSICAL PIECES TO PLAY ON PIANO

Published by
Wise Publications
14-15 Berners Street,
London W1T 3LJ, UK.

Exclusive Distributors:
Music Sales Limited
Distribution Centre, Newmarket Road,
Bury St Edmunds, Suffolk IP33 3YB, UK.
Music Sales Corporation
180 Madison Avenue, 24th Floor,
New York NY 10016, USA.
Music Sales Pty Limited
Level 4, Lisgar House,
30-32 Carrington Street,
Sydney, NSW 2000 Australia.

Order No. AM1012286
ISBN 978-1-78558-403-9

Notes written by Sandy Burnett.

Photographs courtesy of:
Page 3 Photo courtesy of Fernando Aceves
Page 8 Photo courtesy of Stefan Hoederath/Redferns
Page 14 Photo courtesy of C Brandon/Redferns
Page 20 Photo courtesy of Jonatan Gretarsson
Page 24 Photo courtesy of Johan Persson
Page 28 Photo courtesy of Jack Mitchell/Getty Images
Page 32 Photo courtesy of Scott Irvine
Page 36 Photo courtesy of Tabatha Fireman/Redferns
Page 40 Photo courtesy of Michael Leckie
Page 44 Photo courtesy of Stefan Hoederath/Redferns

Every effort has been made to trace the copyright holders
of the photographs in this book but one or two were unreachable.
We would be greatful if the photographers concerned would contact us.

Printed in the EU.

Your Guarantee of Quality
As publishers, we strive to produce every book to the
highest commercial standards.
This book has been carefully designed to minimise awkward
page turns and to make playing from it a real pleasure.
Particular care has been given to specifying acid-free, neutral-sized paper
made from pulps which have not been elemental chlorine bleached.
This pulp is from farmed sustainable forests and was
produced with special regard for the environment.
Throughout, the printing and binding have been planned to
ensure a sturdy, attractive publication which should give years of enjoyment.
If your copy fails to meet our high standards,
please inform us and we will gladly replace it.

www.musicsales.com

WISE PUBLICATIONS
part of The Music Sales Group
London / New York / Paris / Sydney / Copenhagen / Berlin / Madrid / Hong Kong / Tokyo

THE TOP TEN CONTEMPORARY CLASSICAL PIECES TO PLAY ON PIANO

━━

Some people associate classical music very much with the historic past, but there is a wealth of contemporary music out there from a new wave of distinctive and adventurous writers, including plenty of fantastic pieces written for solo piano. Composers include the remarkable Ludovico Einaudi, whose music, rich in spiritual simplicity, has taken the musical public by storm; Jóhann Jóhannsson, who set the classical system to one side as a teenager to kick loose in indie bands; and multi-instrumentalist and composer Yann Tiersen, who similarly broke his violin aged thirteen and never looked back!

Whether you are already familiar with some of these composers or not, we are confident you will love playing their beautiful music – often simple in style, there is something magical about the way these writers make the piano sound. So delve in and enjoy…

BIG MY SECRET
FROM *THE PIANO*

COMPOSER: Michael Nyman
COMPOSED: 1993

One day in the early 1990s, Michael Nyman, who had made his name through his driving, metallic-sounding, high-energy scores written for Peter Greenaway, got a call from a very different kind of movie director. Jane Campion was born and raised in New Zealand, and she wanted to get Nyman on board for her latest film project. It told the story of a mute Scottish woman who had been sold in an arranged marriage to a frontiersman in New Zealand back in the mid-nineteenth century. The film's heroine, Ada, may not have been able to speak, but her real voice was her piano playing; hence the exceptional importance of music in this film. Its title was *The Piano*, and the movie went on to win several awards, including the prestigious Palme d'Or at the Cannes Film Festival – the first time it had ever been won by a female director.

As the composer, Nyman was being asked to strike out in quite a different creative direction here – write lyrical music that would encompass Ada's grounding in Scottish folk music. The end result, 'Big My Secret', is a blend of nineteenth-century salon music and twentieth-century minimalist techniques.

BIG MY SECRET

FROM *THE PIANO*

Michael Nyman

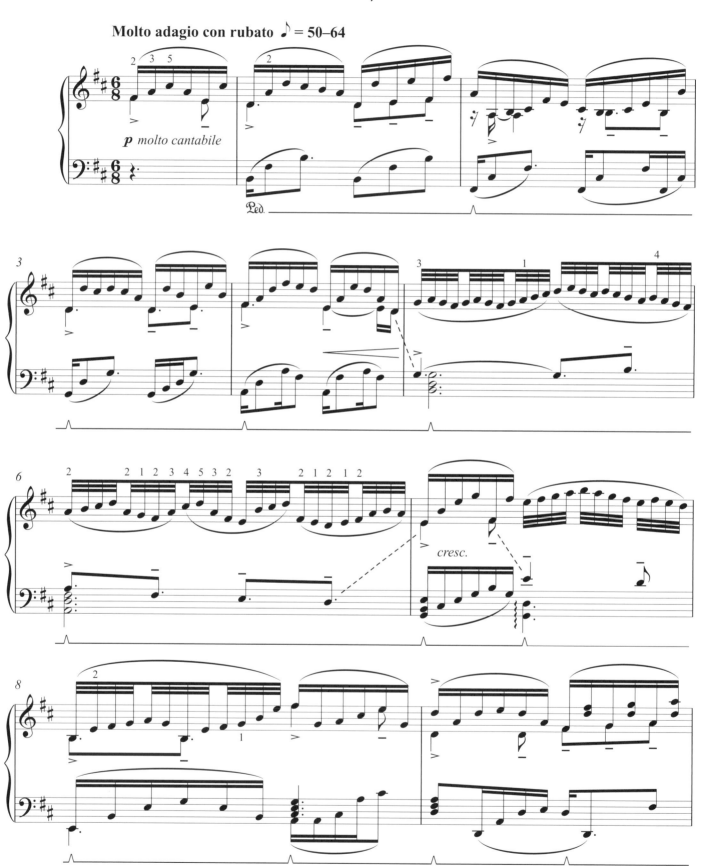

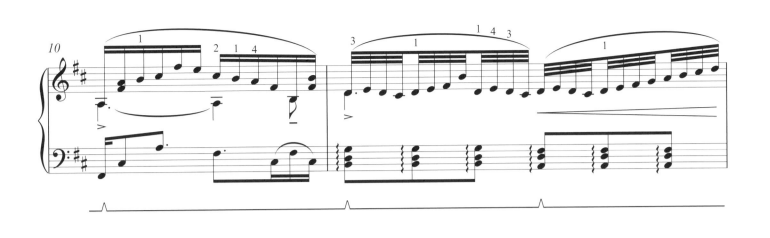

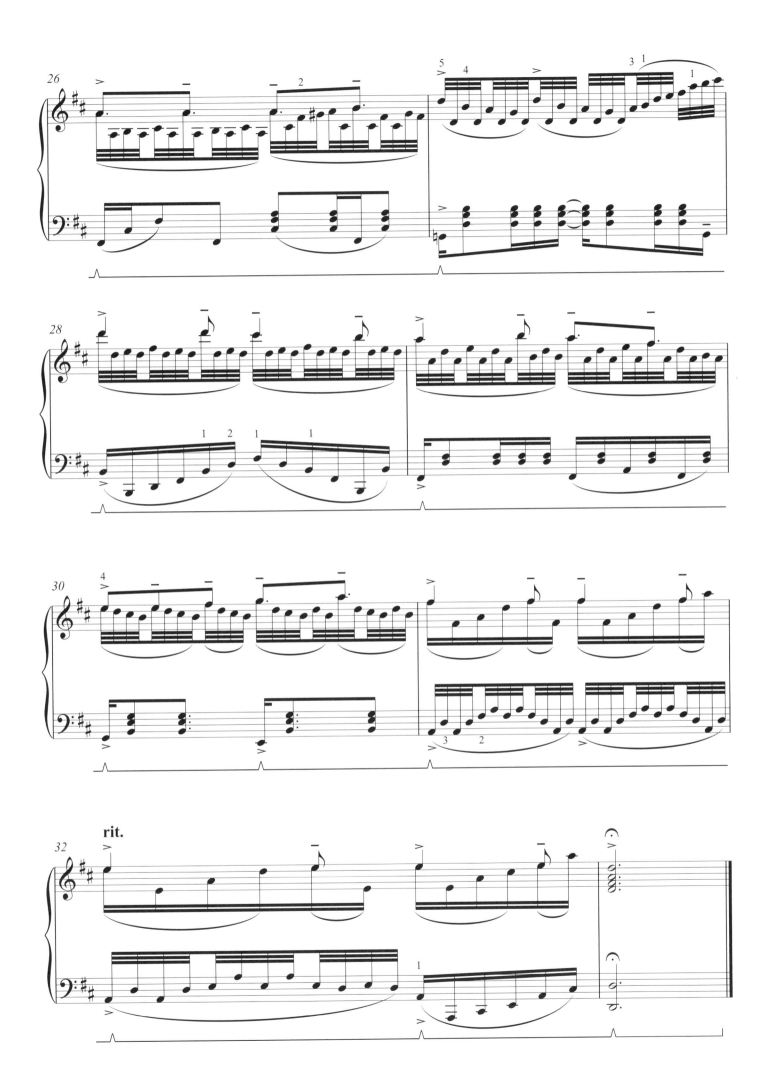

AMBRE

COMPOSER: Nils Frahm
COMPOSED: 2009

The piano has always been central to the work of Nils Frahm. Growing up in a suburb of Hamburg in the eighties and nineties, he studied piano with someone who had himself studied with a protégé of Tchaikovsky, and this awareness of a classical lineage is apparent in his music. However, there's much more besides; a real curiosity about what the piano is capable of, which has, for example, seen him create an album recorded with felt on the hammers and help devise an una corda instrument which has only one string per note, rather than the customary two or three per note in the higher register. This, alongside Frahm's love of analogue recording gear and his desire to make and mend equipment instead of buying new off-the-shelf software, all adds up to a fascinating musician.

'Ambre' is a piano piece that dates from near the start of Frahm's compositional journey. It's the first track on his album *Wintermusik*, originally meant as a Christmas present for his family and friends. In the original recorded version, 'Ambre' is amplified with some discreet sounds on celeste, but this piano solo version is magical enough on its own.

AMBRE

Nils Frahm

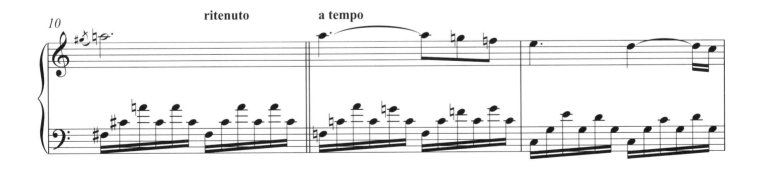

9

ritenuto   a tempo

poco a poco ritardando

COMPTINE D'UN AUTRE ÉTÉ: L'APRÈS-MIDI

FROM *AMÉLIE*

COMPOSER: Yann Tiersen
COMPOSED: 2001

This haunting piece comes from the score of one of the most captivating French films of the early 2000s. *Amélie* stars Audrey Tautou in the title role of a shy and lonely Parisian waitress, whose life changes forever from the day she finds a lost box of a boy's childhood treasures. She does the decent thing, tracks down the box's rightful owner and returns it to him. Thereby she discovers a new meaning for her own life: to be helpful to other people. Shot on a budget of ten million dollars, *Amélie* has taken almost twenty times that at the box office to date, becoming the highest-grossing French-language film ever to be released in the United States.

Amélie's director Jean-Pierre Jeunet had heard Yann Tiersen's music while he was driving one day. He was so taken with it that he bought all of Tiersen's albums, and approached him out of the blue to write the *Amélie* score.

In this reflective number, Tiersen draws on a technique that many a seventeenth-century composer would have been familiar with: taking a four-chord pattern and using it as a basis over which musical ideas can flow. The effect, though, is less historical than contemporary. It sums up the 'here and now' urban world that Amélie lives in: quirky, individual and shot through with a certain Parisian *je ne sais quoi*.

COMPTINE D'UN AUTRE ÉTÉ: L'APRÈS-MIDI

FROM *AMÉLIE*

Yann Tiersen

rit.

a tempo

mp

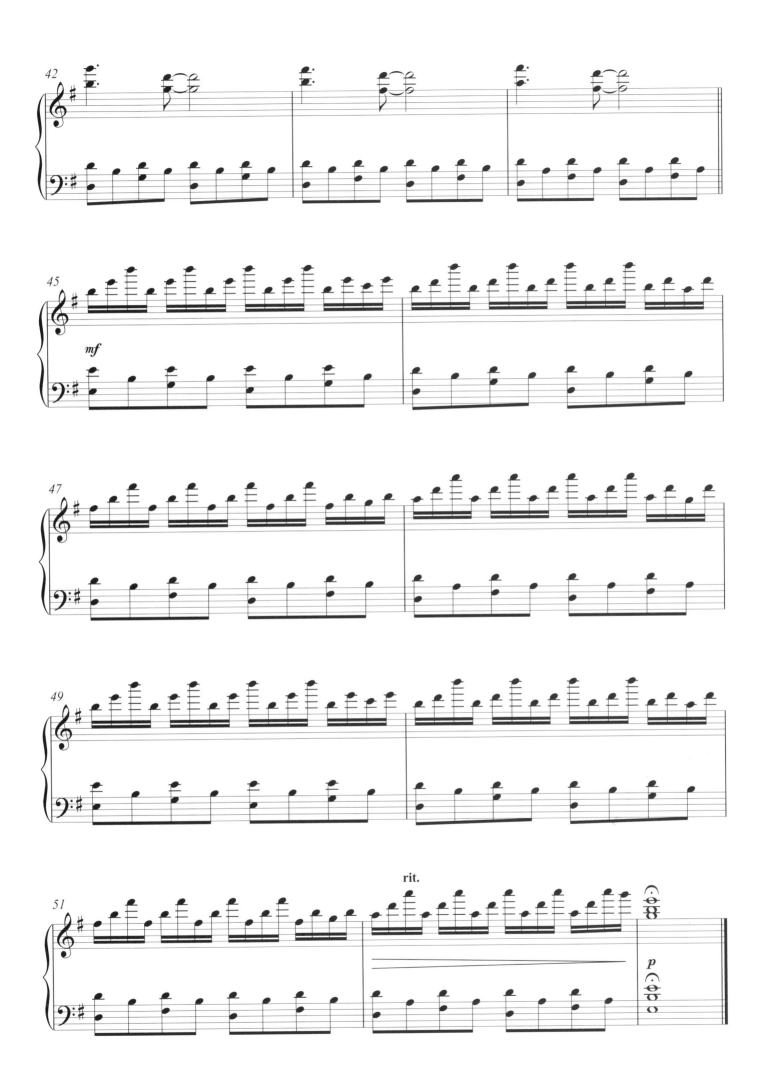

19

FORCES OF ATTRACTION
FROM *THE THEORY OF EVERYTHING*

COMPOSER: Jóhann Jóhannsson
COMPOSED: 2014

One of the most original voices writing for cinema at the moment, Jóhann Jóhannsson was born in Iceland's capital Reykjavík in 1969. After starting out learning to play piano and trombone, Jóhannsson threw the classical system of education and all its constraints aside in favour of playing in indie bands. It was there that he developed an approach which has gone on to be a trademark of his style ever since: combining music played by live instruments with electronic sounds in a layering technique. This strikingly original blend has served Jóhannsson well ever since, from solo albums, to orchestral, theatre, and chamber music, to acclaimed film scores, including

The Theory Of Everything (2015). Based on the life of theoretical physicist Stephen Hawking, it won Jóhannsson a Golden Globe as well as Oscar, BAFTA, Grammy and Critics' Choice nominations for his score.

'Forces Of Attraction' was originally scored for piano with several strata of guitars, six cellos and a mysterious instrument called a Marxophone. The way the music oscillates around a D major tonality shows Jóhannsson aiming for a kind of 1970s English folk sensibility. Given the warmth of the music (and the title of the piece), it should come as no surprise that this is a love theme.

FORCES OF ATTRACTION

FROM *THE THEORY OF EVERYTHING*

Jóhann Jóhannsson

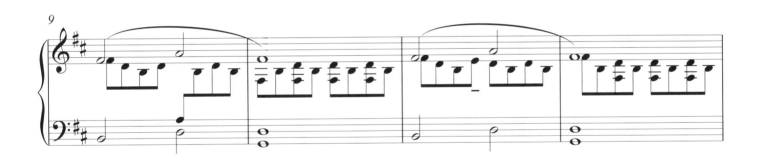

JUNE: TRANSIT OF VENUS
FROM *ONCE AROUND THE SUN*

COMPOSER: Joby Talbot
COMPOSED: 2004

In 2004, Classic FM made Joby Talbot its first ever composer in residence, and asked him to write twelve pieces in twelve months, each one to be broadcast straight away. Talbot accepted the challenge and created an annual cycle of works which he called *Once Around The Sun*. 'Transit Of Venus' is his June piece, and it refers to something magical that he and his wife and son were lucky enough to experience one morning: the planet Venus moving across the face of the Sun, looking like a small black disc, over a period of several hours.

In the original version of the piece, a high, soaring violin carries the main opening melody against a gently repeating broken chord pattern. Here, recast for solo piano, the right hand carries the tune while picking up some of the broken chord figuration that moves in crotchets, then quavers and semiquavers before moving back to the tranquillity of the opening. This piece is an exquisite depiction of a rare and special experience. A transit of Venus is something that happens once or twice in a lifetime, if we're lucky. We'll have to wait until 2117 for the next one.

JUNE: TRANSIT OF VENUS

FROM *ONCE AROUND THE SUN*

Joby Talbot

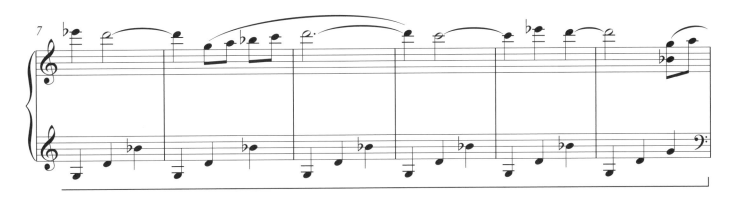

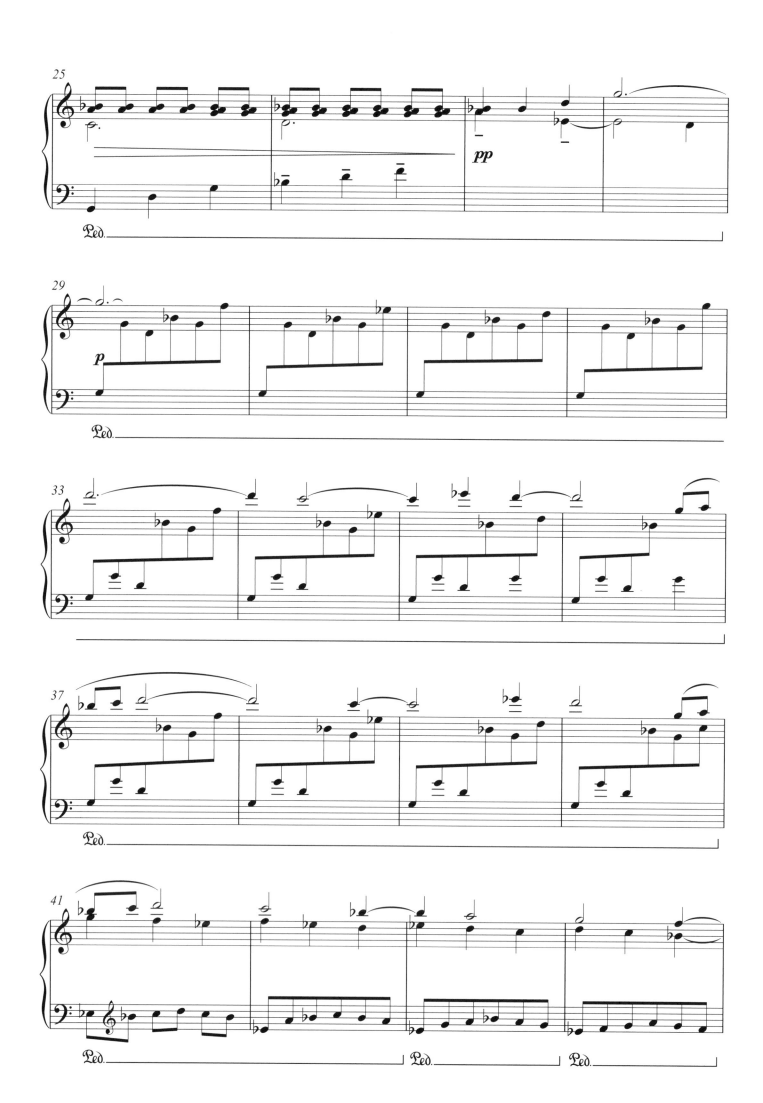

OPENING

FROM *GLASSWORKS*

COMPOSER: Philip Glass
COMPOSED: 1982

Twos against threes, triplets against quavers… The essential tension within every single bar of this piece points to one of the key characteristics of the minimalist style of which he's a leading exponent: repetition, extension, harmonic evolution and a centred stillness. Glass himself isn't a great fan of the term 'minimalism' – he prefers to be thought of as a composer of 'music with repetitive structures' – less snappy, perhaps, but more accurately descriptive. Much of his early work was based on the extended reiteration of brief, elegant melodic fragments that knitted together to form a kind of aural tapestry.

While this piece is for solo piano, *Glassworks* itself is scored for a range of instruments. Right from the outset it was conceived as a recording project – Glass's first album for the CBS record label – and one which aimed to present his music to a wider listening public. There was even a special mix of the music designed to be played on a brand new invention, the Sony Walkman. Music and technology rooted in the early eighties, this is a piece very much of its time.

OPENING

FROM *GLASSWORKS*

Philip Glass

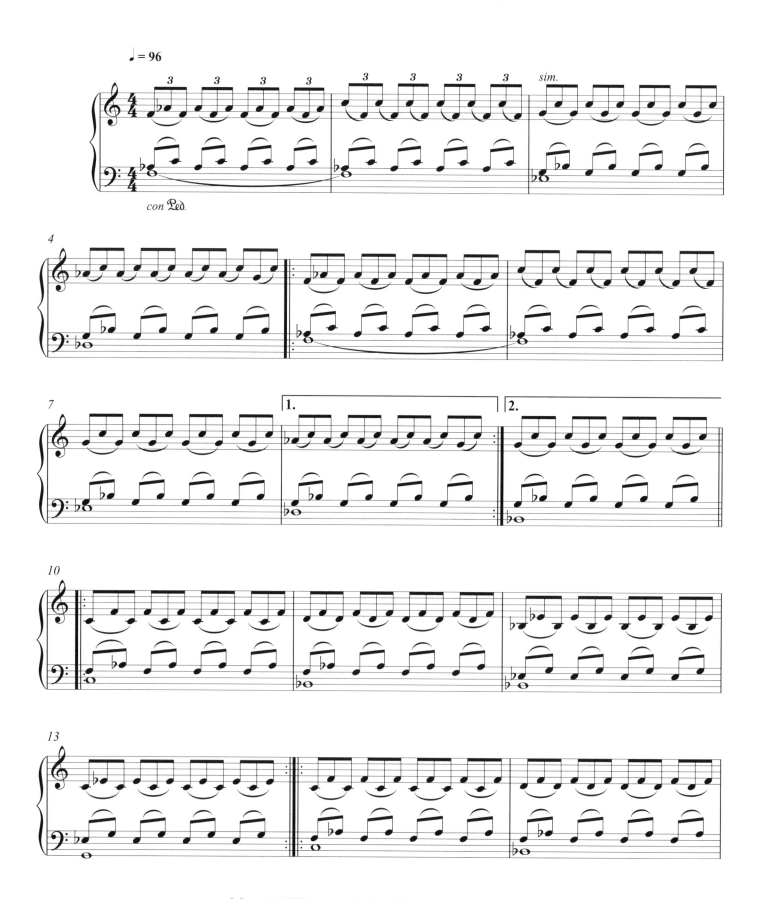

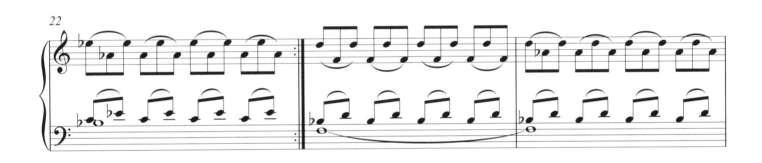

OPUS 26

COMPOSER: Dustin O'Halloran
COMPOSED: 2006

British girl falls for American boy when they meet as students at a Los Angeles university; she overstays her visa and runs into all sorts of problems with US immigration. That's the essential plot of *Like Crazy*, a film starring Anton Yelchin, Felicity Jones and Jennifer Lawrence, the actors largely improvising their dialogue from a script outline co-created by the film's director Drake Doremus. After its premiere at the Sundance Film Festival, *Like Crazy* was awarded the Grand Jury Prize.

Creating the score for the film was pianist Dustin O'Halloran – it's just one of his many film score credits, which also include music for the Sofia Coppola movie *Marie Antoinette*

(2006). Art school, rather than music school, was O'Halloran's training ground, he's recently collaborated with Adam Wiltzie to form an ambient music duo splendidly entitled A Winged Victory For The Sullen, and as a solo artist he's also released four albums, including *Piano Solos Volumes One And Two*.

As a contrast to the emotional dilemma at the heart of *Like Crazy*, 'Opus 26' offers space for spiritual meditation. Freeing the music from traditional bar lines, O'Halloran encourages the performer to create breadth in their interpretation. As he puts it: 'A walking pace, feel the space.'

OPUS 26

Dustin O'Halloran

A walking pace, feel the space

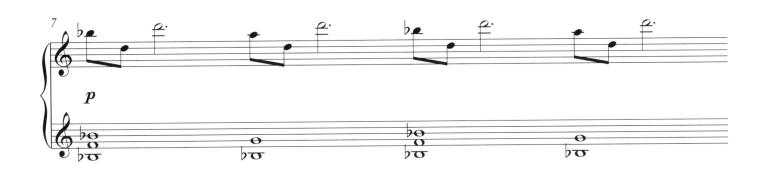

UNA MATTINA

COMPOSER: Ludovico Einaudi
COMPOSED: 2004

In recent years, Einaudi's compositions have captured the hearts of the music-buying public, evoking a space of calm and quietness that is a world apart from the bustle of twenty-first-century life. His own individual voice came to the fore in the 1990s, catching a huge wave of support and interest from the new forces of the internet and social media.

With 'Una Mattina', Einaudi brings us a meditation around the key of A minor. The overall mood is of peace, floating over a flowing sequence of semiquavers or sixteenth notes. Use the pedal to keep the music fluid. Despite the accents towards the end of the piece, maintain the sense of tranquillity, staying within a dynamic that never rises above *mezzo piano*. The piece is the title track of a 2004 Einaudi album and it seems to have an almost timeless quality to it. As the composer says, 'unlike my other albums, it doesn't belong to a time in the past. It speaks about me now, my life, the things around me.'

UNA MATTINA

Ludovico Einaudi

37

THE UNICORN'S HORN
FROM *WOLF HALL*

COMPOSER: Debbie Wiseman
COMPOSED: 2015

If you were looking to name the most successful historical television series of recent times, then *Wolf Hall* would be right up there. Hilary Mantel's Booker-winning novels on the machinations of the Tudor court, with King Henry VIII and his fast-rising right-hand man Thomas Cromwell, made it from page to screen with the help of Peter Straughan, who distilled eleven hundred pages into a grippingly atmospheric six hours of television. As one newspaper reviewer put it, 'this account… feels as real and as visceral as if the wolves of Henry's court were panting down our necks.'

Debbie Wiseman's music played a crucial role in *Wolf Hall*'s success. Usually, composers do their work after the filming has finished, but in this case Wiseman sent demos of her score to director Peter Kosminsky, and he played them on set. Her music informed the actors as they created their roles. Her score features Elizabethan-era instruments such as the lute and harpsichord, but there are moments for the modern piano too, such as this one, 'The Unicorn's Horn'. Against a backdrop of violence and chicanery in the *Wolf Hall* story, this theme represents a moment of calm and tenderness.

THE UNICORN'S HORN

FROM *WOLF HALL*

Debbie Wiseman

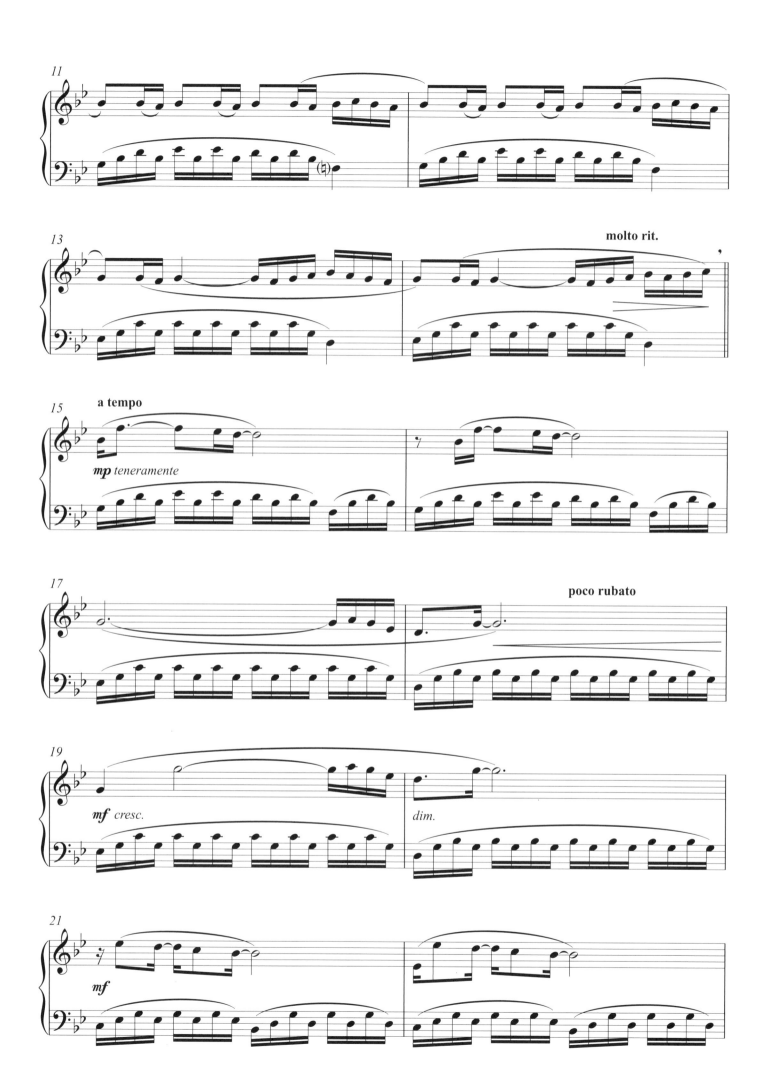

molto rit.

a tempo

mp teneramente

poco rubato

mf cresc.

dim.

mf

VLADIMIR'S BLUES

COMPOSER: Max Richter

COMPOSED: 2003

Whether he's writing for concert hall, stage or film, Max Richter draws on both the classical tradition and several other musical genres of the moment, including punk, electronica, minimalism and spoken word. Two examples of Richter's approach recently grabbed the public imagination; he reworked Vivaldi's famous *Four Seasons* for the twenty-first century, using phasing and looping techniques, and he wrote an eight-hour piece called 'Sleep', which was transmitted by the BBC in one gigantic overnight broadcast.

'Vladimir's Blues' is right at the other end of the scale – a tiny piece that takes just over a minute to play, with oscillating figures in the right hand and long notes tolling like bells in the left. Does this piece hint at tranquillity, or is there something unsettling in its stillness? It comes from *The Blue Notebooks* in which Richter recorded material he'd written during the build-up to the Iraq War in 2003. He conceived it as 'a protest album about Iraq, a mediation on violence – both the violence that I had personally experienced around me as a child and the violence of war, at the utter futility of so much armed conflict.'

VLADIMIR'S BLUES

Max Richter

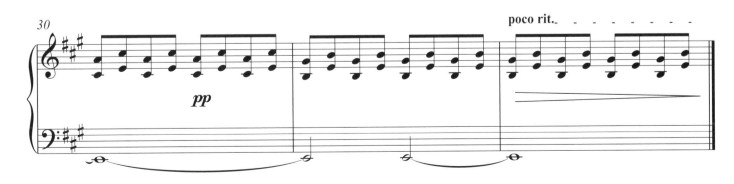

123456789

THE TOP TEN...

THE **TOP** TEN
CLASSICAL PIECES
EVERY BEGINNER
PIANIST
SHOULD LEARN
AM1012231

THE **TOP** TEN
MOST BEAUTIFUL
PIECES TO PLAY
ON PIANO
AM1012253

THE **TOP** TEN
CHRISTMAS
SONGS TO PLAY
ON PIANO
AM1012484

THE **TOP** TEN
LOVE SONGS
TO PLAY
ON PIANO
AM1012275

THE **TOP** TEN
PIANO SONGS
OF ALL TIME
AM1012242

THE **TOP** TEN
CONTEMPORARY
CLASSICAL PIECES
TO PLAY ON PIANO
AM1012286

THE **TOP** TEN
MOST CALMING
PIECES TO PLAY
ON PIANO
AM1012319

THE **TOP** TEN
FILM THEMES TO
PLAY ON PIANO
AM1012264

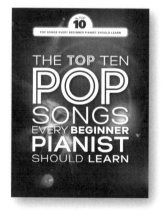

THE **TOP** TEN
POP SONGS EVERY
BEGINNER PIANIST
SHOULD LEARN
AM1012297

THE **TOP** TEN
JAZZ SONGS TO
PLAY ON PIANO
AM1012308